EDINBURGH

This I-SPY book belongs to:_____

Introduction

Let's start at the beginning. Edinburgh Castle, perched high on its volcanic rock, is where this grand, historical city began. Explore the Castle to see cannons and treasures before setting out on your adventure back in time to the Medieval Old Town. Follow the narrow streets in the footsteps of kings and queens, inventors, scientists, poets, murderers, thieves and witches, all coming to life through their homes, stories and museums.

Having reached the "World's End" of the Old Town you can move forward to the Georgian New Town. Not that it's very new – it was started in 1765! – well-designed with statues, parks and gardens, galleries and classical buildings. Across the city, visit many super family attractions including Our Dynamic Earth, the Royal Yacht Britannia, the Museum of Childhood and the Zoo. For a bird's eye view over the city, climb Arthur's Seat and Calton Hill. Edinburgh is said to be the only city where you can walk around and only go uphill, so take it easy on an open-top bus tour, jumping on and off at the famous sites. Remember to look out for traditional Scottish icons such as bagpipes and haggis.

As the World's first Unesco City of Literature, Edinburgh celebrates famous local writers from Robert Louis Stevenson to J K Rowling, who created Harry Potter. Find the cafes where she wrote her Wizardry stories and a gravestone that inspired one of her characters.

There are exciting places to see on day trips out of town: spy the magnificent Forth Bridge, the Seabird Centre at North Berwick and step on board the supersonic Concorde at the Museum of Flight.

There's always something exciting happening in and around Edinburgh. In summer you will find street jugglers, stilt walkers and musicians entertaining huge crowds during the International and Fringe Festivals. In December it's a sparkling Winter Wonderland with Christmas trees, lights, outdoor ice rink, fair-rides and Big Wheel. You are sure to have great fun, whenever you visit Edinburgh!

How to use your I-SPY book

The book is arranged by area to help you get the most out of your visit, the map on pages 62 and 63 will help you achieve this. As you explore, don't forget to tick off the sights – as you see them. You need 1000 points to send off for your I-Spy certificate (see page 64) but that is not too difficult because there are masses of points in every book. As you make each I-Spy, write your score in the box and, when there is a question, double your score if you can answer it. Check your answers against the correct one on page 63.

EDINBURGH CASTLE

Perched high on its volcanic rock, the Castle dominates the city skyline. For centuries the home of Scottish kings and queens, its various styles tell of changing uses, from siege (defence) to attack.

I-SPY points: 10

Date: _____

MONS MEG

A giant siege gun given to James II of Scotland in 1457 – one of the world's oldest cannons. Weighing over 6,000kg and very difficult to move, she averaged just 5km (3 miles) per day whilst being transported.

I-SPY points: 15

Date: _____

ONE
O'CLOCK
GUN

FIRED EVERY DAY, EXCEPT SUNDAYS, AT ONE O'CLOCK. THE FIRST GUN WAS FIRED IN 1861 TO PROVIDE AN AUDIBLE TIME SIGNAL FOR SHIPS IN THE PORT OF LEITH.

ONE O'CLOCK GUN

A time signal to help sailors at sea comprising of dropping a time ball on the top of Nelson Monument, Calton Hill and the firing of the gun at exactly one o'clock.

I-SPY points: 15, double if you see the gun fired

Date: _____

ST MARGARET'S CHAPEL

The oldest part of the Castle. Having fled the 1066 Norman invasion, Margaret married King Malcolm III of Scotland but died broken hearted when he and their son were killed. Her son King David I built the chapel. She was made a saint in 1250.

I-SPY points: 15

Date: _____

THE GREAT HALL

Built for James IV, he had little chance to enjoy it. He was killed at the Battle of Flodden in 1513. It has one of only two medieval roofs left in Scotland. Can you spy the spy hole?

I-SPY points: 20

Date: _____

THE HONOURS OF SCOTLAND

The crown, sceptre and sword dating from the late 15th century are displayed in the Crown Room. They were first used together at the coronation of Mary Queen of Scots in 1543. She was only nine months old and cried throughout the ceremony.

I-SPY points: 20

Date: _____

WITCHES' WELL

At the entrance to the Castle Esplanade, a wall fountain commemorates the place where over three hundred women were burned at the stake, accused of being witches.

I-SPY points: 15

Date: _____

CANNONBALL HOUSE

17th-century house at Castle Wynd North named because of the cannon ball stuck in its wall. Supposedly fired from the castle during the Jacobite siege, it more likely marks the height for the first piped water supply in 1676.

I-SPY points: 10, double if you can spot the cannon ball!

Date: _____

SCOTCH WHISKY EXPERIENCE

This visitor attraction's swirling barrel ride explains the process of making Scotland's most famous export. It also houses the world's largest collection of Scotch Whisky.

I-SPY points: 10

Date: _____

GOOSE-PIE HOUSE

In 1743 the poet Allan Ramsay had the unusual octagonal Ramsay Lodge built. Unfortunately his friends told him it looked like a goose pie – much to his annoyance!

I-SPY points: 15

Date: _____

CAMERA OBSCURA

This pinhole camera is Edinburgh's oldest purpose-built visitor attraction, intriguing people for over 150 years. In the World of Illusions you can become a giant or swap heads with your friends!

I-SPY points: 10

Date: _____

THE HUB

The towering 1845 former Highland Tolbooth St John's Church is the home of the Edinburgh International Festival – one of the world's most important cultural events.

I-SPY points: 10

Date: _____

GLADSTONE'S LAND

Thomas Gledstanes bought this house in 1617. You can discover the lives of his tenants and what the Old Town was like 400 years ago. The family emblem, a hawk, can be seen outside.

I-SPY points: 10

Date: _____

LADY STAIRS CLOSE

Robert Burns, the famous Scots bard, came to Edinburgh when his first book was published in 1786. While the house he stayed in on Baxter's Close has gone, a plaque marks the spot.

I-SPY points: 15

Date: _____

IN A HOVSE
ON THE EAST SIDE OF THIS CLOSE,
ROBERT BVRNS
LIVED DVRING HIS FIRST VISIT
TO EDINBVRGH, 1786.

WRITERS' MUSEUM

Lady Stair's House includes the printing press for Scott's Waverley Novels, Robert Louis Stevenson's riding boots and even a plaster cast of Robert Burns' skull.

I-SPY points: 10

Date:

BRODIES CLOSE

This Lawnmarket Close is named after Deacon Brodie, a respectable cabinetmaker and Councillor by day and burglar by night. He inspired the story of *Dr Jekyll and Mr Hyde*.

I-SPY points: 10

Date:

ROYAL MILE

The Royal Mile isn't a street or a mile. It's a number of streets stretching from the Castle to the Palace of Holyroodhouse. This distance set the former Scots Mile, which was slightly longer than the mile we have now.

I-SPY points: 10

Date: _____

DAVID HUME

David Hume (1711-1776) was born in the Lawnmarket, near his statue on the High Street. He attended Edinburgh University aged just 12 and went on to become the greatest philosopher in the English language.

I-SPY points: 10

Date: _____

LAST PUBLIC HANGING

A brass plaque at the corner of the High Street marks the spot where on 21st June 1864, George Bryce was hanged for the murder of Jane Seaton. The last public execution in Edinburgh.

I-SPY points: 10

Date: _____

HEART OF MIDLOTHIAN

Near St Giles' Cathedral is a heart shaped pattern of stones. It marks the position of the 15th-century Tolbooth, the administrative centre of the town, prison and one of several sites of public execution.

I-SPY points: 15

Date: _____

MARY KING'S CLOSE

Hidden beneath the Royal Mile lie a few narrow streets built over in 1753. Now a visitor attraction where you can see one of the streets that time forgot – and even meet some of its residents!

I-SPY points: 20

Date: _____

ST. GILES' CATHEDRAL

This landmark on the Royal Mile has a distinctive 49m (161ft) crown steeple. The site has been a major religious focal point for around 900 years.

I-SPY points: 5

Date: _____

EDINBURGH AWARD

In the quadrangle of the City Chambers there is a stone with the handprints of the recipients of the Edinburgh Award.

I-SPY points: 10

Date: _____

JAMES BRAIDWOOD STATUE

The Father of the British Fire Service. He was famous for his bravery during the Great Fire of 1824, which left around 450 families homeless around the High Street.

I-SPY points: 15

Date: _____

MERCAT CROSS

Beside St Giles' Cathedral was the market's historic meeting place for proclamations on General Elections and Royal marriages. Announcements are still made here three days later than in London – the time to travel to Edinburgh on horseback.

I-SPY points: 10

Date: _____

ADAM SMITH

Adam Smith (1723-1790), the Father of Economics, was born in 1723. His statue near St Giles' Cathedral looks over the water to his birthplace in Fife.

I-SPY points: 10

Date: _____

LOCH NESS MONSTER

Nessie does not live in Edinburgh, but you can learn about the world's favourite mystery at the 3D Loch Ness Experience in the High Street.

Where in Edinburgh was the Nor' Loch?

I-SPY points: 10, double with answer

Date: _____

OLD FISHMARKET CLOSE

Described around 1800 as "a steep, narrow stinking ravine" with fish "thrown out on the street" and "dragged down by dirty boys or dirtier women; and then sold unwashed ... from old, scaly, rickety tables". It has changed quite a bit since then!

I-SPY points: 15

Date: _____

FRINGE SOCIETY

In the High Street is the home of the Edinburgh Festival Fringe – the largest arts festival on the planet.

I-SPY points: 10

Date: _____

ANCHOR CLOSE

The Encyclopaedia Britannica began here in 1768. The idea of an engraver and a printer, they appointed William Smellie to write it in 100 weekly parts, priced 6d (about 2p).

I-SPY points: 15

Date: _____

WELLHEAD

There are a number of wellheads around the Old Town. Until 1820 these were the only way that thousands of residents could get water.

I-SPY points: 10

Date: _____

GHOST TOURS

A number of ghost tours start from the High Street and cover historical incidents, folklore and life in the overcrowded 17th-century Old Town.

I-SPY points: 10

Date: _____

HEAVE AWA' HOUSE

In 1861 the 17th-century building at 97-99 High Street suddenly fell down, killing everyone except one young boy, Joseph McIvor. His rescuers heard him shout from the rubble "Heave Awa Lads I'm no deid yet".

I-SPY points: 15

Date:

BRASS RUBBING CENTRE

In the rebuilt Trinity Apse – part of a church founded around 1460 near what's now Waverley Station – you can make rubbings from brasses including medieval knights and Celtic designs.

I-SPY points: 10

Date:

MUSEUM OF CHILDHOOD

The first in the world to be dedicated to the history of childhood. Set in two 18th-century buildings it's full of toys and also looks at growing up, from schooldays to holidays.

I-SPY points: 10

Date: _____

MOUBRAY HOUSE

The oldest occupied building in Edinburgh, with parts dating from the 1400s. Daniel Defoe, the author of Robinson Crusoe lived here. He was an English spy.

I-SPY points: 10

Date: _____

JOHN KNOX HOUSE

Dating back to 1470, this was home to James Mosman, goldsmith to Mary, Queen of Scots. The religious reformer John Knox may have died here in 1572.

I-SPY points: 10

Date: _____

SCOTTISH STORYTELLING CENTRE

Sitting alongside John Knox House, the centre presents an exciting programme of live storytelling, theatre and literature.

I-SPY points: 10

Date: _____

WORLD'S END

The protective 16th-century Flodden Wall and Netherbow Port stood near here. Beyond was the separate burgh of the Canongate. For Edinburgh citizens this was the world's end.

I-SPY points: 15

Date: _____

I-SPY points: 10

Date: _____

OLD CHILDREN'S BOOKSHELF

This shop at 175 Canongate is said to have the largest selection of second-hand children's books in Scotland. Can you find any old I-Spy books in here?

MUSEUM OF EDINBURGH

This museum is in Huntly House, a series of 16th- to 18th-century buildings. By 1851 they were so sub-divided that 323 tenants lived here! It's now a treasure box of objects from the capital's past.

I-SPY points: 10

Date: _____

PEOPLE'S STORY

Housed in the 1591 Canongate Tolbooth, this museum looks at the lives of Edinburgh's ordinary people and includes a wartime kitchen, bookbinder's workshop and former jail.

I-SPY points: 10

Date: _____

ROBERT FERGUSSON STATUE

Standing outside Canongate Kirkyard is "Scotland's forgotten poet". He inspired Robert Burns but died tragically young at only 24 in 1774.

I-SPY points: 10

Date: _____

GIRTH CROSS

The circle of paving stones near the foot of the Canongate marks the site of the Girth Cross. Here in 1600 the beautiful Lady Warriston was beheaded for murdering her husband.

I-SPY points: 15

Date: _____

SCOTTISH PARLIAMENT

This complex, controversial building is built from steel, oak and granite. The shapes on the windows have been compared to curtains, hairdryers and even Scalextric controllers!

I-SPY points: 5

Date: _____

OUR DYNAMIC EARTH

Here you can take an interactive journey through the planet's past, present and future. From the Big Bang to the stars with glaciers, dinosaurs, volcanoes, rain forests and icebergs along the way.

I-SPY points: 10

Date: _____

ARTHUR'S SEAT

This extinct volcano rises 251m (823ft) above Holyrood Park, with great views from the top. Here James Hutton the "Father of Modern Geology" studied the rocks.

Which "Kingdom" can you see from the top of Arthur's Seat?

I-SPY points: 5, double with answer

Date: _____

PALACE OF HOLYROODHOUSE

This is the official residence in Scotland of Her Majesty The Queen. The baroque palace is perhaps best known as the home of Mary, Queen of Scots.

I-SPY points: 10

Date: _____

THE SANCTUARY STONE

Find an "S" marker near the junction of Abbey Strand. This shows the boundary of the Abbey Sanctuary, a zone inside which debtors were free from the threat of arrest.

I-SPY points: 15

Date:

QUEEN MARY'S BATHHOUSE

This curious little building is said to have been where Mary, Queen of Scots would bathe in white wine. It was once attached to the Royal garden wall and it was more likely a summerhouse.

I-SPY points: 15

Date:

EVERYMAN

This colourful Stephan Balkenhol sculpture is outside the Council Headquarters in East Market Street. Inspired by Pop Art, the sculpture of an unremarkable man becomes far more mysterious.

I-SPY points: 15

Date: _____

COWPARADE

CowParade is a worldwide public art event with cows appearing in 'unmoosual' places. Two graze on the roof of the Council Headquarters in East Market Street (Hint – you may need to be higher up to spy them).

I-SPY points: 15

Date: _____

SCOTSMAN HOTEL

This turreted building on North Bridge housed The Scotsman newspaper for nearly a century. Originally it had lofts for carrier pigeons carrying news from outlying parts of Scotland.

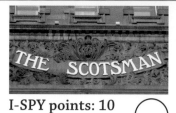

I-SPY points: 10

Date:

CITY ART CENTRE

This towering former warehouse has a collection of Scottish art and regularly changing exhibitions. Past events have even included costumes from the Star Wars films.

I-SPY points: 10

Date:

FRUITMARKET GALLERY

This 1938 fruit and vegetable market has been a gallery since 1974, showing world-class contemporary art alongside its café and bookshop.

I-SPY points: 10

Date:

EDINBURGH DUNGEON

A scary visitor attraction with 11 actor-led shows and 2 rides capturing 500 years of dark history, from haunted catacombs, torture chambers and body snatchers to cannibals.

I-SPY points: 10

Date: _____

HALFWAY HOUSE

A tempting stop on the long climb up the steps of Fleshmarket Close, between Market and Cockburn Streets. This is Edinburgh's smallest pub and one of the smallest in Britain.

I-SPY points: 15

Date: _____

J K ROWLING COFFEE HOUSES

J K Rowling wrote parts of the first Harry Potter novel in coffee houses at 6 Nicolson Street and 21 George IV Bridge.

I-SPY points: 20 each

Date: _____

SURGEONS' HALL MUSEUM

Learn about the history of the study of anatomy. Here in Nicolson Street, body snatchers Burke and Hare brought bodies to sell for medical research – but when corpses were in short supply they turned to murder.

I-SPY points: 10

Date: _____

FESTIVAL THEATRE

Edinburgh's oldest theatre site, here since 1830 and associated with ballet since the first International Festival in 1947. Behind the glass front is the older Empire Palace.

I-SPY points: 10

Date: _____

NATIONAL MUSEUM OF SCOTLAND

The Museum has been collecting exhibits for 200 years and has displays covering everything from ancient civilisations to science and technology.

I-SPY points: 10

Date: _____

GEORGE HERIOT'S SCHOOL

Founded by a bequest from the Royal goldsmith in 1628, the school is said to be the inspiration for Hogwarts of the Harry Potter novels.

I-SPY points: 15

Date: _____

WILLIAM TOPAZ McGONAGALL
(1825-1902)

Hailed as the worst poet in English, he is buried in Greyfriars Kirkyard. Hogwarts' Professor McGonagall is named after him!

I-SPY points: 20

Date: _____

GREYFRIARS BOBBY

Spy the statue of this famous wee dog. After his master died in 1858, faithful Bobby kept constant watch over his grave for 14 years.

I-SPY points: 15

Date: _____

FRANKENSTEIN

This pub on George IV Bridge is named after Mary Shelley's monster. Victor Frankenstein visits Edinburgh in the novel.

I-SPY points: 10

Date: _____

NATIONAL LIBRARY OF SCOTLAND

The National Library is Scotland's largest with around 16 million printed items, 2 million maps, 32,000 films and three miles of manuscripts!

I-SPY points: 10

Date: _____

MAGGIE DICKSON

Maggie was tried and hanged in the Grassmarket in 1724 but as her body was taken away to be buried there was knocking from within the coffin. She was alive, but under Scots law legally dead and so set free and lived for a further 40 years! Find the pub named after her.

I-SPY points: 15

Date: _____

WHITE HART INN

This Grassmarket pub is named for the events of 1128 when King David I was thrown from his horse and injured whilst hunting a huge white stag. Visitors have included Burns and Wordsworth.

I-SPY points: 15

Date: _____

CORDINER'S LAND

The stone panel on the West Port shows the ancient emblem of the Cordiner's Guild – from French for shoemaker, "cordonnier". Improvements to building design gave the residents better space and ventilation.

I-SPY points: 10

Date: _____

ROYAL LYCEUM THEATRE

Originally built as the New Lyceum in 1883 at a cost of £17,000, its popularity caused it to be renamed, 'stealing' the royal away from the Edinburgh Theatre Royal.

I-SPY points: 10

Date: _____

USHER HALL

Built using a bequest of £100,000 from whisky distiller Andrew Usher in 1896, it opened in 1914 and has hosted musicians from all over the world.

I-SPY points: 5

Date: _____

PIPER

The Great Highland Bagpipe is the national instrument of Scotland and famous all over the world.

I-SPY points: 15

Date: _____

HAGGIS

The haggis is not an animal but a savoury pudding. Famously praised in Robert Burns' poem, it's eaten at suppers to celebrate his birthday.

I-SPY points: 15

Date: _____

EDINBURGH INSPIRING CAPITAL

This highlights the attractions of the city region as a place to live, visit and study.

I-SPY points: 15

Date: _____

KILTED DOORMEN
The doormen at some hotels wear kilts – even at the ultra-fashionable Missoni hotel.

I-SPY points: 20

Date: _____

POLICE BOX
Bigger than your average Dr. Who "TARDIS", designed by the City Architect in the 1930s to complement the city's classical architecture.

I-SPY points: 15

Date: _____

SALTIRE
This is the flag of Scotland, also known as The Saint Andrew's Cross – an association going back to a battle in 832 AD. It was in use as a national flag from 1542.

I-SPY points: 10

Date: _____

TARTAN GIFT SHOPS

Tartan everything! Scotland has many different tartans that identify the clans. There is no shortage of gift shops.

I-SPY points: 5

Date: _____

WHISKY SHOP

There are specialist shops that sell whisky – a wee bit of distilled Scotland. Whisky made in Scotland is sometimes referred to as Scotch.

I-SPY points: 5

Date: _____

VINTAGE BUS TOURS

A vintage open-top bus – a great way to spy things – and see a different perspective of the city.

I-SPY points: 10

Date: _____

SIR JAMES YOUNG SIMPSON

A statue of the Scottish doctor (1811-1870) and discoverer of the anaesthetic effect of chloroform is in West Princes Street Gardens.

I-SPY points: 15

Date:

ROSS FOUNTAIN

This fountain in West Princes Street Gardens was made near Paris, shown at the 1862 London Exhibition and then shipped to Edinburgh in 122 pieces.

I-SPY points: 10

Date:

ALLAN RAMSAY

A statue of the poet (1686-1758) stands in West Princes Street Gardens. He started the first lending library.

I-SPY points: 15

Date:

THE MOUND

The Mound is a man made hill formed from digging of the foundations for the New Town. It took 2 million cart loads!

I-SPY points: 10

Date: _____

NATIONAL GALLERIES OF SCOTLAND

The National Galleries complex is home to a collection of fine art from early Renaissance to late nineteenth century and special international exhibitions.

I-SPY points: 10

Date: _____

WORLD HERITAGE SITE

The Old and New Towns and their special relationship make this a World Heritage Site. It is marked by a plaque in the Mound precinct.

I-SPY points: 15

Date: _____

SCOTT MONUMENT

This Gothic skyrocket is a monument to Edinburgh-born writer Sir Walter Scott (1771-1832). It is over 61 metres (200 feet) high and has 64 statues of characters from his books.

How many steps to the top?

I-SPY points: 10, double with answer

Date: _____

DAVID LIVINGSTONE

A statue of the Scottish explorer (1813-1873) is in East Princes Street Gardens. H M Stanley met him in Africa with the famous words – "Dr Livingstone, I presume?".

I-SPY points: 15

Date: _____

BALMORAL HOTEL

Landmark hotel at 1 Princes Street with its Michelin-starred restaurant. The "J K Rowling Suite" is where the author finished writing *Harry Potter and the Deathly Hallows*.

I-SPY points: 10

 Date: _____

WELLINGTON MONUMENT

This statue of the Duke of Wellington near Waterloo Place was sculpted by Sir John Steell. When unveiled in 1852 the press proclaimed it "the Iron Duke in bronze by Steell".

I-SPY points: 10

 Date: _____

42

NATIONAL MONUMENT

Inspired by the Acropolis in Athens, it commemorates the lives lost in the Napoleonic Wars.

I-SPY points: 10

Date: _____

NELSON MONUMENT

This stone telescope was planned within a month of Admiral Horatio Lord Nelson (1758-1805) being killed at the Battle of Trafalgar in 1805.

I-SPY points: 15

Date: _____

OLD CITY OBSERVATORY

Inspired by a Greek temple of the Four Winds, the building was designed by William Henry Playfair in 1818.

I-SPY points: 15

Date: _____

BURNS MONUMENT

A monument to the national bard, Robert 'Rabbie' Burns (1759-1796) on Regent Road designed in 1830 in the style of a Greek Temple – in keeping with Edinburgh's reputation as the "Athens of the North".

I-SPY points: 15

Date: _____

PLAYHOUSE THEATRE

Built in 1929 with 3,048 seats, the Playhouse is Scotland's largest and most opulent theatre-cinema.

I-SPY points: 15

Date:

DREAMING SPIRES

This sculpture by Helen Denerley in Picardy Place is of two huge scrap metal giraffes. They are more commonly called Martha and Gilbert!

I-SPY points: 15

Date:

ROCKSTAR NORTH

The home of video games such as *Lemmings* and *Grand Theft Auto* Series is at Calton Square, just off Leith Street.

I-SPY points: 15

Date:

THE MANUSCRIPT OF MONTE CASINO

Edinburgh born Sir Eduardo Paolozzi's sculpture is in front of St Mary's RC Cathedral. It looks part human, part machine and is about pilgrimage.

I-SPY points: 15

Date: _____

SIR ARTHUR CONAN DOYLE

Scottish physician and writer (1859-1930) was born in Picardy Place. Spy either the pub named after him or the statue of his famous creation, Sherlock Holmes.

I-SPY points: 15, double points for both

Date: _____

OPEN EYE GALLERY

I-Spy the Open Eye. This art gallery promotes an exciting range of young and established artists.

I-SPY points: 10

Date: _____

SCOTTISH NATIONAL PORTRAIT GALLERY

This "Caledonian Temple of Fame" was begun in 1882. The external sculptures of eminent Scots took 17 years to complete.

I-SPY points: 10

Date: _____

ROBERT LOUIS STEVENSON

Famous writer Robert Louis Stevenson (1850-1894) lived at 17 Heriot Row.

Which of his books features Long John Silver?

I-SPY points: 15, double with answer

Date: _____

BUTE HOUSE

Charlotte Square is the official residence of The First Minister of Scotland.

I-SPY points: 5

Date: _____

GEORGIAN HOUSE

Discover high society living and "life below stairs" in the 18th-century New Town.

I-SPY points: 10

Date: _____

PRINCE ALBERT MEMORIAL

This memorial, unveiled in 1876, sits in Charlotte Square Gardens, home to the Edinburgh International Book Festival.

I-SPY points: 5

Date: _____

ALEXANDER GRAHAM BELL

Name ring a bell? Alexander Graham Bell (1847-1922) inventor of the telephone was born at 16 South Charlotte Street.

I-SPY points: 15

Date: _____

SIR WALTER SCOTT

The "Wizard of the North" (1771-1832) lived at 39 North Castle Street. He filled the rooms with old pikes, armour and books.

I-SPY points: 15

Date: _____

KENNETH GRAHAME

Kenneth Grahame (1849-1932), author of *Wind in the Willows* first published in 1908, was born in 32 Castle Street.

I-SPY points: 15

Date: _____

NORTHERN LIGHTHOUSE BOARD

George Street is an unlikely place for a lighthouse but there is one above the door of the Board headquarters.

I-SPY points: 15

Date: _____

ASSEMBLY ROOMS

In March 1858 Charles Dickens (1812-1870) gave a reading of his *Christmas Carol* novel here.

I-SPY points: 15

Date: _____

JAMES CLERK MAXWELL

The work of the Edinburgh born physicist and mathematician (1831-1879) is compared with Newton and Einstein. His statue is at the east end of George Street.

I-SPY points: 10

Date: _____

50

MELVILLE MONUMENT

This monument is to Henry Dundas, Viscount Melville, an aristocratic 18th-century politician so powerful he is known as "The Uncrowned King of Scotland".

I-SPY points: 10

Date: _____

NEW REGISTER HOUSE

3 West Register Street is where events like births, deaths and marriages are recorded. The Register Office has been here since 1855 and has 6.5km (4 miles) of shelving in its dome.

I-SPY points: 10

Date: _____

ROYAL BOTANIC GARDEN

More than 70 acres of beautifully landscaped gardens and Britain's tallest palm house.

I-SPY points: 15

Date: _____

WATER OF LEITH WALKWAY SIGN

The riverside Walkway is a ribbon through the city and provides easy access to the Modern Art Galleries.

I-SPY points: 15

Date: _____

ST. BERNARD'S WELL

On the Water of Leith Walkway between Dean Village and Stockbridge, this Well is an open pillared dome with a statue of Hygieia, Goddess of Health.

I-SPY points: 20

Date: _____

DEAN VILLAGE

This picturesque former village on the Water of Leith was a milling hamlet for more than 800 years.

I-SPY points: 15

Date: _____

6 TIMES

6 life-size figures by Antony Gormley is positioned between the National Gallery of Modern Art and the sea at Leith Docks.

I-SPY points: 15 each

Date: _____

THE SCOTTISH NATIONAL GALLERY OF MODERN ART

This Art Gallery at Belford Road was the first in Britain dedicated to collecting 20th-century works of art.

I-SPY points: 15

Date:

EDINBURGH ZOO

The zoo has been in its 82 acres of parkland at Corstorphine Road since 1913. It's home to over 1,000 rare and endangered animals.

I-SPY points: 10

Date:

PORTOBELLO BEACH

Edinburgh's seaside with its promenade, sandy beach and amusement arcades is a great place to enjoy a few hours of fun.

I-SPY points: 20

Date: _____

ROYAL YACHT BRITANNIA

For 40 years this famous ship served the members of the Royal Family. Now berthed at Ocean Terminal, Leith, you can go on board and explore this fine ship.

I-SPY points: 20

Date: _____

HAWES INN

Sitting in the shadow of the Forth Bridge in South Queensferry, this inn was where Robert Louis Stevenson wrote part of his famous novel, *Kidnapped*.

I-SPY points: 20

Date: _____

FORTH BRIDGE

Opened in 1890, the railway
bridge spans the Firth of Forth.
This Scottish landmark is an
engineering marvel held together
by more than 8 million rivets.
When it was completed it was the
longest cantilever bridge in the
world and remained so in 1917.

I-SPY points: 15

Date:

DEEP SEA WORLD

Scotland's national aquarium at
North Queensferry, where you
can walk through an underwater
tunnel and swim with sharks.

I-SPY points: 15

Date:

FIREWORKS

There are huge firework displays in every season that light up the skies.

I-SPY points: 20

Date: _____

STREET PERFORMERS

Both the Fringe and Winter Festivals attract street performers of all types.

I-SPY points: 20

Date: _____

WINTER WONDERLAND

In winter, Edinburgh sparkles and there are attractions like the Big Wheel and ice rink in Princes Street Gardens.

I-SPY points: 25

Date: _____

BUTTERFLY AND INSECT WORLD

Just off the City By-pass near Sherrifhall, this is the place to learn about creepy crawlies and handle tarantulas, snakes and millipedes.

I-SPY points: 15

Date: _____

SCOTTISH MINING MUSEUM

Put on a "magic helmet" and learn all about Scotland's mining heritage at the Lady Victoria Colliery, Newtongrange.

I-SPY points: 15

Date: _____

CONCORDE

See supersonic Concorde and much more at the National Museum of Flight, East Fortune Airfield.

I-SPY points: 20

Date: _____

ROSSLYN CHAPEL

Founded in 1446 this is a jewel of the mason's art and star of the *Da Vinci Code*.

Solve the chapel's murder mystery. Who killed the Apprentice?

I-SPY points: 20, double with answer

Date: _____

BASS ROCK

A crag off North Berwick, home to the largest single gannet colony in the world.

How many gannets nest on the island?

I-SPY points: 25, double with answer

Date: _____

LUCA'S ICE CREAM VAN

There is even a Rolls Royce ice cream van! Look out for it at events or at the seaside.

I-SPY points: 20

Date: _____

SCOTTISH SEABIRD CENTRE

This unique centre at North Berwick harbour is a world leader in remote wildlife viewing.

I-SPY points: 20

Date: _____

Index

First published by Michelin Maps and Guides 2011 © Michelin, Proprietaires-Editeurs 2011. Michelin and the Michelin Man are registered Trademarks of Michelin. Mapping based on Ordnance Survey of Great Britain with the permission of the Controller of Her Majesty's Stationery Office © Crown Copyright 100000247. Created and produced by Blue Sky Publishing Limited. All rights reserved. No part of this publication may be reproduced, copied or transmitted in any form without the prior consent of the publisher. Print services by FingerPrint International Book production – fingerprint@pandora.be. The publisher gratefully acknowledges the contribution of Vivien Devlin in the production of this title. In addition, the contribution of the I-Spy team: Camilla Lovell, Geoff Watts and Ruth Neilson. The publisher also gratefully acknowledges the contribution and assistance of the following who supplied pictures for this title: Kenneth J Scott, Deep Sea World, Edinburgh Butterfly & Insect World, Historic Scotland, Rosslyn Chapel Trust, Royal Zoological Society of Scotland and Unitaw Limited. Other images in the public domain and used under a creative commons licence. All logos, images, designs and image rights are © the copyright holders and are used with kind thanks and permission.
10 9 8 7 6 5 4 3 2 1

P16: Loch Ness Experience, Princes Street Gardens; P25: Arthur's Seat, The Kingdom of File; P41: Scott Monument, 287 steps; P47: Robert Louis Stevenson, Treasure Island; P59: Rosslyn Chapel, The Master Mason; P59: Bass Rock, 150,000 gannets.

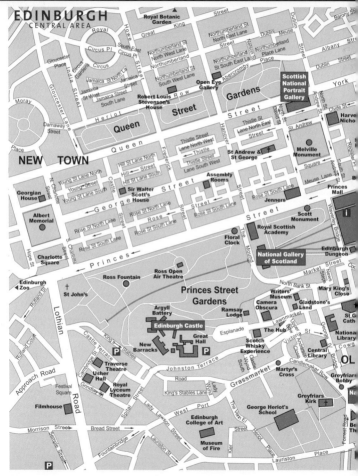

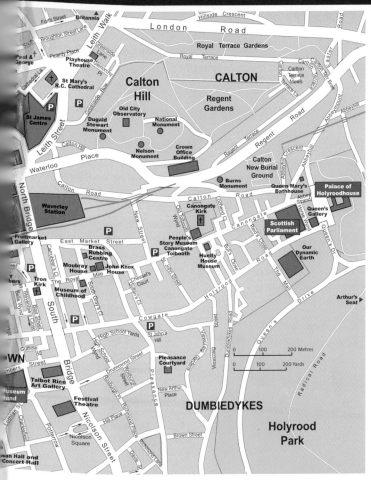

HOW TO GET YOUR I-SPY CERTIFICATE AND BADGE

Every time you score 1000 points or more in an I-Spy book, you can apply for a certificate

HERE'S WHAT TO DO, STEP BY STEP:

Certificate

- Ask an adult to check your score
- Ask his or her permission to apply for a certificate
- Apply online to www.ispymichelin.com
- Enter your name and address and the completed title
- We will send you back via e mail your certificate for the title

Badge

- Each I-Spy title has a cut out (page corner) token at the back of the book
- Collect five tokens from different I-Spy titles
- Put Second Class Stamps on two strong envelopes
- Write your own address on one envelope and put a £1 coin inside it (for protection). Fold, but do not seal the envelope, and place it inside the second envelope
- Write the following address on the second envelope, seal it carefully and post to:

I-Spy Books
Michelin Maps and Guides
Hannay House
39 Clarendon Road
Watford
WD17 1JA

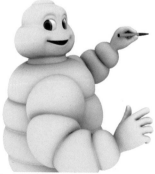